The Blue Heron Tree

The Blue Heron Tree

By Edith Thacher Hurd

Illustrated by Clement Hurd

THE VIKING PRESS NEW YORK

This book is dedicated to all those members of the San Francisco Bay area Audubon societies who have worked so hard to preserve the blue heron trees of this story and who are still working to save the feeding grounds of the Bolinas Lagoon at Bolinas, California.

 First published in 1968 by The Viking Press, Inc., 625 Madison Avenue, New York, N.Y. 10022. Published simultaneously in Canada by The Macmillan Company of Canada Limited. Library of Congress catalog card number: 68-16064. Printed in U.S.A. by R. R. Heywood Company.

598 1. Birds
2. Nature
3. Herons

Contents

End of Winter

The band-tailed pigeons flew across the deep canyon. Then, swinging together, they turned to land in the branches of the tallest redwood tree.

Wakened by the pigeons, a small screech owl who had been sleeping there after her night of hunting opened one eye.

A black raven circled the redwood.

A squirrel leapt from branch to branch, her bushy tail flicking now backward, now forward, as she moved up the tall tree.

Winter was coming to an end, leaving the ground soaked with the rain that had fallen day after day. There had not been a winter like this for many years. The wind, bellowing in from the ocean, had whipped the quiet lagoon into whitecaps, and the redwoods had been wrapped in cold fog.

But now, at last, the rain stopped as the wind shifted from the southwest to the west. This west wind was the wind of spring and summer, for as the sun moved northward each day it warmed the water of the ocean and the ocean warmed the wind blowing over it.

On the morning that the band-tailed pigeons disturbed the small sleeping owl, the sun shone above the canyon for the first time in many weeks. Sunlight touched the top of the tall redwood tree and moved down, branch by branch. A feeling of warmth spread through the damp canyon as the sun flickered into dark corners, under old logs, and into deep thickets.

The air was filled with the smells of spring: of things drying, opening, pushing up from the ground to unfurl themselves to the new brightness.

The pigeons clung to the highest branches of the tallest redwood tree to catch this first sunlight. The squirrel held herself still, to be warmed. But the little owl squeezed her big eyes shut even tighter. The night was her world.

Everywhere in the canyon there was a sense of waiting, a stillness which seemed to hold a promise. The waiting did not last long, for the first shadow, like a dark arrow, sailed into the canyon very early that year.

Big Blue

Big Blue came, like the sun, from the east. His long neck tucked back, his yellow bill forward, his legs trailing rudder-like behind, the huge bird rose over the rim of the canyon and slipped into the gentle air current flowing up from below.

The band-tailed pigeons flapped from the tall redwood tree.

The screech owl woke suddenly.

The high-soaring raven croaked its welcome as the first of the great blue herons returned to the rookery.

The black shadow of the great bird cut across the branch where the little squirrel sat watching.

Big Blue moved slowly as his eyes searched the empty nests in the tall trees far below him. Then, with a hoarse *auk, auk,* he flew on toward the quiet lagoon that lay at the end of the canyon.

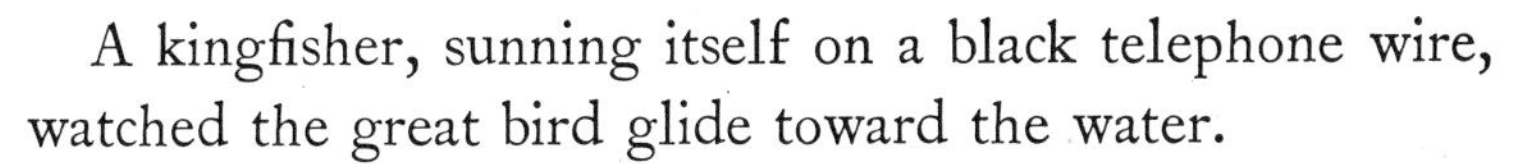

A kingfisher, sunning itself on a black telephone wire, watched the great bird glide toward the water.

A ruddy duck stopped in mid-dive.

A willet looked up from the mud flat where it poked with its long bill, hunting for shrimp.

A flock of small sandpipers rose together, frightened from the shore by the heron.

Big Blue banked for landing by lowering his long legs and spreading his wings, as if holding himself against his own flight. His feet touched the water. His wings closed to his sides. His long neck stretched upward. The great blue heron stood tall and motionless in the shallow water of the lagoon.

If it had not been for the lagoon, neither the herons nor the egrets would have returned year after year to raise their young in the tall trees of the canyon.

The lagoon, protected from the wind and waves of

the ocean, was a rich feeding ground. The herons and egrets fished there, and many other birds came to rest and to feed on their way north in the spring for their nesting and south in the fall for the winter.

But the peaceful lagoon had not always been there. Once, a long, long time ago, it had been a deep valley with a river flowing to the sea. It was a time when far to the north the earth was covered with ice and snow. There had been many glaciers. But when a warmer time came, the glaciers melted and the sea rose. It spread over the shore and flooded the valleys.

And so the swift-running river flowing through the valley had become a quiet lagoon. Strong ocean currents dropped sand and small stones at its mouth until the entrance was only a narrow opening. The tide flowed through this opening, filling and emptying the lagoon twice each day.

Small streams running from side canyons had brought soil or silt to fill the lagoon, so that now, when the blue herons fed at low tide, only slow-running channels of water meandered between the mud flats.

The rising tides covered the mud flats and brought food—tiny plankton, known as "the grass of the sea"—to feed the worms, the shrimps, the clams, and the crabs that lived in the soft mud and along the shore. Small fish swam in the shallow water of the channels. The great herons, the egrets, the fast-flying birds, the long-legged willets,

the sandpipers, the fat little ruddy duck, and even the tiniest ghost crabs found plenty to eat in the quiet lagoon.

Now Big Blue moved slowly forward. As the tide emptied the lagoon, his sharp eyes searched the water running against his long legs.

He cocked his head. His long neck shot forward. He opened his bill to snap at a minnow. The small fish turned in the scissor-like beak. Big Blue stretched his neck and the fish was gone.

A ring-billed gull followed the big bird, squawking every time the heron held a fish in his bill. A graceful tern dove again and again until Big Blue made a great show of wing-flapping and uttered his deep *auk, auk*. After that the tern fished for itself at a greater distance.

Two ducks, a bufflehead and a canvasback, paddled about in the shallow water close to the heron. A stiff-necked grebe dove in the deeper water while along the mud flats the willets and sandpipers poked for worms and hunted for shrimps.

Big Blue fished for a long time, wading slowly through the water. He placed his black clawlike feet with care, one after the other, as he walked against the tide.

He stopped, standing very still for a few moments. His head tilted. His neck shot forward. The sharp bill closed on a small crab.

When Big Blue had eaten his fill, he spread his wings, moving them with a strong, easy motion in order to raise himself out of the water and into the air.

At first he glided close to the surface; then he rose slowly, higher and higher. He swung his long legs up under his body, pulled his neck back into an *S* position, and making a wide circle, headed toward the canyon.

Big Blue flew straight to the tallest redwood tree, where the small screech owl still slept. The squirrel scampered

up through the lacy green branches to a spot where she could watch the heron without being seen.

A bold Steller's jay screeched at the big bird, who seemed to hold the canyon in a sort of magic spell whenever his shadow fell across the tall trees.

Big Blue Chooses a Nest

Big Blue landed in the nest at the top of the tallest redwood tree. He stood a long time, his head raised, his long neck stretched toward the sun overhead. The wind flowing up from the lagoon to the low mountains that stood a short distance behind the canyon ruffled his gray feathers. From that day on until the end of the nesting season, this great flat platform would belong to Big Blue. He would defend it as his territory and it was here that he would raise his young.

Big Blue began to repair the platform after the winds and rain of winter. He ducked and poked. His head bobbed. He twisted his neck this way and that as he pulled branches, twigs, and bits of rotten wood out of the nest and dropped them over the side.

Big Blue had not been working long when a second dark shadow cut across the canyon, then another and another. There were four birds in this first group. Big Blue watched as they glided, just as he had, over the rim of the canyon and down toward the redwood trees that made up the rookery. Then he returned to his nest-building.

The largest of the new arrivals, an unusually strong young heron with a huge spread of blue wings, flew to the tall tree where Big Blue was at work. The young heron stepped cautiously from branch to branch. He stood tall, straight, bold, one foot almost touching the nest.

Big Blue continued his work.

Then suddenly he lunged from the edge of the platform. Caught by surprise, the young heron lost his balance. He swayed a moment, then, half raising his wings, steadied himself.

Big Blue and the young heron plunged at each other with long, sharp bills. A hoarse croaking rumbled in their throats. The hollow clacking of their beaks echoed in the quiet rookery.

The two necks twisted and turned. Back feathers rose. Long neck feathers stiffened into bristling collars.

The squirrel dashed higher up the tree. Coming as close

as she dared to the two birds, she chattered wildly, her little voice rising to a high squeak. She sat quivering as Big Blue struck again and again from the firm platform of his nest.

The young heron strained to reach the high platform, but each blow threw him off balance. The swaying branch shifted beneath him.

Big Blue leaned forward. Stretching his long neck over the edge of the nest, he struck swiftly and hard. The young heron stepped back to escape the flashing beak. His sharp claws lost their hold. He fell backward. Opening his wings, he glided to a nearby tree.

The bill-clacking stopped. The deep croaking died away. The gray squirrel darted to the ground, frisking with excitement. Quiet returned to the canyon.

Four or five new herons flew into the canyon each morning. Big Blue defended his territory over and over again until, one by one, the new herons had chosen other nests.

Now there were long days of waiting while the birds prepared for the female herons, always last to arrive at the rookery.

In the woods and along the hillside, wild iris bloomed, purple and white. Fetid adder's-tongue spread spotted leaves and opened delicate brown flowers.

At the bottom of the canyon a little stream ran quietly where once a strong river had tumbled and roared as it carried the soil of the mountain down to the sea. For many

years the river cut into the sandstone rock of the mountain, softening, cracking, pulling, digging deeper and deeper until at last the water carved out a narrow canyon and filled it with the rich, moist soil the redwoods needed in order to grow. Now, at the time when Big Blue came to nest in the tall tree, the small stream meandered beneath the great redwoods. As it made its way to the lagoon, the water formed quiet pools, some cool and shaded by the tall trees, some warmed by the spring sun.

In one of these pools an orange-bellied newt swam around and around with a small brown female. Sometimes they swam deep in the pool. Sometimes they nosed gently into the muddy bank. The newt held the small female with his dark-colored sandpaper-like feet. The sun shone on the pool. The newt, moving his head from side to side, stroked the little brown female.

The willows standing beside the pool had turned yellow, and the pussy willows had begun to push open their sticky buds.

It was a time of quiet and waiting while the spring grew stronger each day.

New Arrivals

One morning, when the sun had just touched the top of the tallest redwood tree and Big Blue stood to catch its first warmth, the female herons flew into the canyon.

Gliding in from the east, their long beaks glistening in the sunlight, they circled the canyon in slow flight. Each chose a tree and landed to rest and to wait.

A few of the females were greeted by a soft, gentle cooing; others, driven off with bill-clacking and wing-flapping, were forced to search for a mate in some other tree.

Big Blue watched from his platform but he did not accept any of the birds that came toward him.

More females arrived each day; none gained a place in the nest at the top of the tall redwood tree.

Day after day Big Blue sat beside his nest. The warmth of the sun sank through his feathers. Spring was everywhere in the canyon now.

Noisy frogs made a cheerful croaking. They had already left small black eggs, wrapped in a safe covering of clear jelly, in the quiet sunny places of the little stream. A few tiny tadpoles wiggled with new life.

A fence lizard lay on a rock in the sunshine, warming its blue belly.

A slender salamander stirred its four tiny feet, swished its small tail, and crept out from under the rotten log where it had lain cold and still all winter long. It crawled slowly into the bright spring world.

Blue hound's-tongue blossomed under the buckeyes, oaks, and madrone trees on the sunny south slope of the canyon. On the opposite side, green ferns unfurled their delicate fronds in the cold darkness beneath the bay trees and tall Douglas firs.

Big Blue waited. Sometimes he sat with his neck drawn in and his long yellow beak thrust forward. Sometimes he stood with his plumage spread wide, the feathers of his neck hanging like a soft gray beard. Running his beak over his back in long, soothing motions, he preened himself in the sun.

At other times Big Blue worked on his nest, adding small branches and twigs or pulling out old ones and dropping them over the side.

Most of the other herons had danced their courtship dance, mated with the bird they had chosen to share their nest, and were already sitting on two or three greenish-blue eggs. But still Big Blue waited, hunched, beak thrust forward, alone.

In the deep thicket of the wood, a doe wandered restlessly. It was almost time for her fawn to be born.

The gray squirrel had found an old woodpecker's hole in a den-tree and was busy lining it with soft grass and bits of fur from her own coat.

The Most Beautiful Heron

Big Blue had been feeding at the lagoon all morning. When he finished, he rose slowly from the water and headed back toward the canyon. His sharp eyes looked down at the small fish swimming against the strong tide.

Suddenly Big Blue caught sight of a female heron flying toward the lagoon.

The great blue heron circled closer and closer to the new arrival. The young female dipped to the water and Big Blue returned to his nest.

Big Blue watched and waited. It was a long time before the young heron reappeared. Balancing herself gracefully on the wind, her blue-gray wings scarcely moving, she passed over the tops of the trees and landed gently on a branch close to the nest in the top of the tall redwood tree.

Big Blue stood straight and tall in the nest; his beautiful plume feathers rose. The morning sun flooded over him, turning his neck feathers into a collar of silver. He made a soft sound deep in his throat.

Watching the big heron carefully, the female moved along the swaying branch. She too raised her head in the air. Her back and neck feathers rose and she stood like this for a long time. Then she stepped off the branch and into the nest of the great blue heron.

Big Blue leaned forward; his beak touched the soft feathers. The two birds locked bills. Swaying gently back and forth, they circled the nest. Then their necks crossed, each stroked the wings and back of the other, and they danced their first courtship dance together.

The young heron did not leave Big Blue's nest after that, and it was not long before they were mated.

At the Nest

Although Big Blue had worked hard to prepare the nest, now he spent almost all his time, except when he and the young heron were feeding together at the lagoon, in gathering sticks. Sometimes he twisted live, green twigs from the branch of a redwood tree. Sometimes he carried sticks from the floor of the canyon to his mate at the nest. She, in turn, brought branches and twigs for Big Blue to twine and poke into the flat, pancake-like platform.

The tall redwood tree where Big Blue and the female heron worked at their nest stood in the middle of the deep canyon. Its curving branches touched those of the other redwoods, weaving a soft, green cover to catch the sunlight, the rain, and the fog. Little sun ever reached

the shaded, damp floor of the canyon, where the stream flowed quietly between moss-covered rocks. Tough sword ferns grew in this dark world, but few flowers ever found their way through the deep covering of brown, rotting branches that had fallen from the trees overhead.

Very often during the summertime a warm wind from the sea blew through the canyon and over the low coastal mountains beyond. The mountains chilled the warm wind and turned it to fog. The wet fog curled like a wandering ghost among the brown tree trunks and the green branches. The branches held the wet fog, letting it fall, drop by drop, to the ground below.

In the wintertime heavy rain fell in he canyon. The rain, the wet fog, and the stream kept the deep canyon cool and moist all through the year and provided everything the redwoods needed. The tall trees had grown in this canyon and others like it for many hundreds of years.

Day after day passed and the canyon lay still and quiet, with only an occasional *auk, auk* when one heron mistook another's platform for his own.

Four tiny fur balls slept in the squirrel's nest in the old den-tree.

The newborn fawn hid in the secret places of the canyon while his mother kept guard from a safe distance.

The screech owl had less time for sleep now with four mouths to fill.

The Steller's jay left its own nest to scream in the quiet spring mornings. The black raven soared through the canyon, its small fearsome shadow following below.

Poppies burst from the ground, spattering orange and yellow across the rocky hillsides. Lupine washed in blue waves over the meadows above the canyon.

In the little pool close to the willow tree, tiny newts and black tadpoles had burst from the jelly-like eggs.

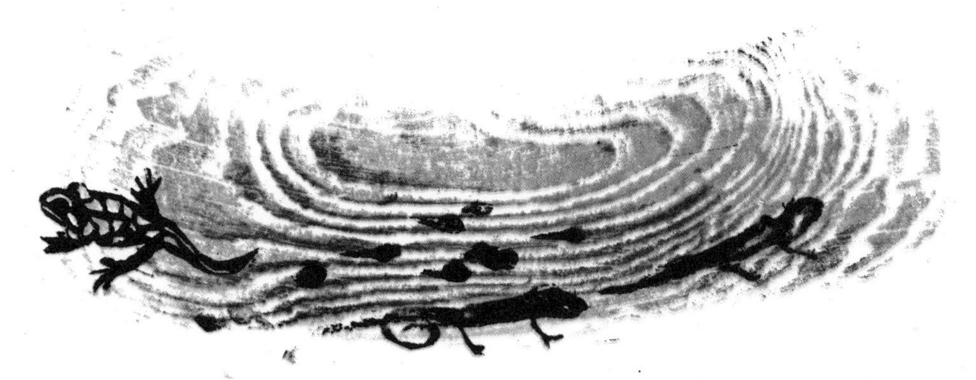

Then came the egrets.

Floating into the canyon on beautiful, gleaming wings, the birds filled the green trees with soft balls of white.

Once more the canyon turned into a noisy hunting ground. The egrets were driven from nest to nest as the herons defended their platforms with sharp bill-clacking and wing-flapping. It was several days before all the egrets had found unoccupied platforms, accepted mates, and settled down.

Big Blue continued to bring a stick or twig each time he returned to the nest at the top of the tallest redwood tree. The young female took the stick, making a soft cooing sound deep in her throat. By poking and pushing, or by removing an old stick, she found a place for the new one.

Then at last, on a quiet spring afternoon, when Big Blue flew in from the lagoon where he had been feeding for a long time, he saw that the young heron was not standing any more but sat quietly on the nest.

Big Blue flew toward the tree. Swinging his legs forward as he banked against the wind with outspread wings, he landed on a branch beside the platform. The young heron rose to take the stick he offered. Big Blue saw the single egg she had covered.

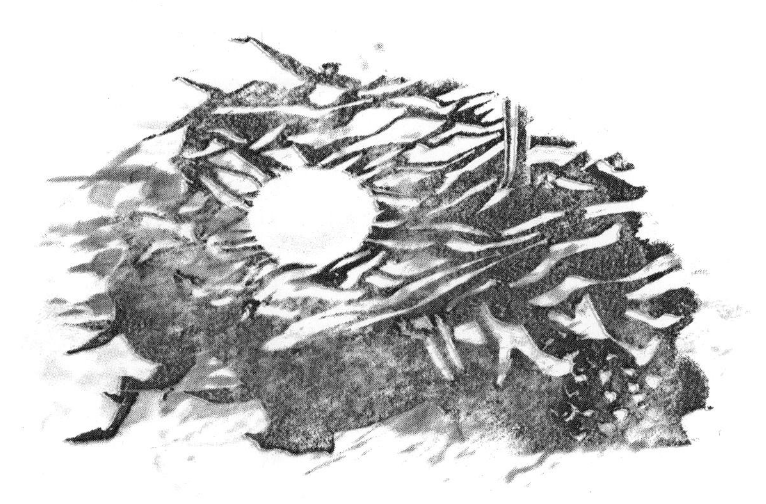

The Robber

From that day on, Big Blue and his mate never left the nest at the same time. While one fed, the other watched over the three greenish-blue eggs that now lay in the center of the platform.

A mound of soft feathers kept the eggs warm through the cold spring nights and protected them from the raven, the hawk, and the jay in the daytime, and the stealthy raccoon during the night.

But not all the nests were guarded as carefully as Big Blue's; and one morning the black raven dove!

It dropped from the sky so fast that one old heron, who was sunning herself only a short distance from her nest, could not reach her eggs in time to protect them.

The raven flew up, up, soaring into the sky. A glint of blue-green showed in its half-open beak.

The egrets, alarmed by the attack, rose in a snow-white cloud and circled the canyon.

The herons stood tall on their platforms, huge wings flapping. Hard, rasping cries broke the morning quiet. Bills snapped, clacking danger.

Big Blue, sitting while his mate fed, held to his nest. When one raven dove, two or more watched from dark places at the edge of the canyon.

The young female heron flew from the lagoon, speeding swiftly on her strong wings.

Big Blue rose to show her that it had not been their nest the raven had visited.

The young heron stood for a long time at the edge of the nest.

The wild-flying egrets settled onto their platforms once more.

Neither the robber nor any other raven disturbed the rookery again that morning.

Baby Birds

The spring grew warmer each day. Buckeyes, growing on the sunny slopes of the canyon, unfolded their smooth leaves. Blossoms, like white candles, stood among the green branches.

In the nest at the top of the tallest redwood tree the young heron felt a stirring. One of her eggs had been cracked.

A tiny bill poked into the sunlight. A skinny body pulled itself out of the shell.

Big Blue stood at the edge of the nest and watched as, one after another, the three babies came into the world.

They were ugly, wet little things, but the sun warmed them and dried their down-covered bodies.

The little birds sprawled in the nest, free at last of the shells that had held them so tightly for twenty-six days.

Opening and closing their beaks, they gulped the new air into their bodies. Then they lay still. The mother heron lowered herself over the three babies and they slept for a long time.

At first the small birds ate only the partly digested food which Big Blue or the mother heron poured, like white soup, down their throats, but it was not long before they were able to swallow bits of fish and small crabs.

The babies grew stronger each day; pushing their way out from beneath the soft feather covering, they tottered about over the rough twigs of the platform. By raising their wings they were able to steady themselves on their thin legs, although they often lost their balance and tumbled over one another.

Two of the birds grew very fast, and it was not long before they were able to move about on their big awkward feet without falling. Gray pinfeathers replaced the first soft down. A rumpled cap of black feathers covered their heads.

The third baby heron was small. He did not grow as large or as fast as the others and he was not very strong.

Now almost every redwood in the canyon held at least three or four nests, and in each nest two or three young herons or egrets clamored to be fed. The rookery became noisy with the clacking of bills and the endless squawking of the hungry little birds.

As soon as it was safe to leave the baby herons alone in the nest, Big Blue and the mother heron fished for long hours each day. When one of them returned to the nest, the two larger birds reached up with their bills to grab at the tall heron's neck. Holding the neck tightly, they pumped up and down with quick, rough jerks, pulling this way and that until a fish slid from the big heron's throat. Sometimes one of the young herons was able to catch the food in his bill; sometimes the fish fell to the platform. When this happened there was a wild tug of war, one bird pulling at the head, the other at the tail.

Seesawing back and forth, they circled the platform until the winner managed to swallow the fish whole.

The smallest bird never fought with the others. He waited for a tiny shrimp or crab that had fallen to the bottom of the nest and been missed by the larger birds.

Danger

Spring moved slowly toward summer.

Blue forget-me-nots sprinkled themselves through the woods and the monkey flower opened its sticky yellow face to the hot sun.

The squirrel taught her young the best roads to travel through the redwoods and up the sunny side of the canyon to the oak trees, where small acorns were already forming for next winter's storage.

The small screech owls had flown from the nest. The mother owl dozed quietly through the late spring days.

The little fawn wandered beside his mother as she browsed, nibbling the scrub oak in the woods, the wild lilac and chamise on the hillsides, and the fresh grass of the meadows high above the deep canyon. The fawn's coat had turned to a golden red. White spots covered his back, making him almost invisible when he moved through the woods. He was like a patch of spring sunlight as he poked at his mother, hungry for her milk.

The stream grew less noisy; no rain had fallen for several months and the water ran slowly through the bottom of the canyon.

Baby salamanders swam in the quiet stream or hid in damp places under rocks and green ferns. The blue-bellied lizard baked itself in a pool of hot dust.

Quiet days passed, when the wind made only a soft rustling in the tops of the trees.

A monarch butterfly floated from one side of the canyon to the other without moving its orange-and-black wings.

The sky was filled with spring stars when it grew dark.

But one night the wind rose. With the wind came fog—not the white wisps that wandered amongst the trees on a summer morning, but a black, wet fog that blew in from the ocean. It hung in the trees like cold winter rain and fell like rain from the high branches to the wet ground below.

No birds rustled in their nests. The animals kept to their rock caves and tree hollows.

Big Blue and the mother heron, their feathers ruffled and puffed to protect them from the cold, hunched themselves on a branch close to their young.

Then, so quietly that it was almost no noise at all, there

came a soft scratching. Two eyes shone at the edge of the platform.

The young birds opened their bills, clacking in the stillness.

Big Blue rose on his long legs but the tiny sparks that had been eyes were gone. The scratching of claws on the thick bark grew fainter. Black fog rolled over the trees.

As the sky brightened, the sun shone weakly on the big platform.

The smallest heron was not in the nest.

By the time the fog cleared from the trees, the raccoon had hidden itself in a cave under a great rock on the cold dark side of the canyon. It was already asleep after its night of hunting.

The mother heron rose and unfolded her strong wings. Catching the wind, she glided toward the ground below, moving in and out among the low branches. She did not return to the platform for the rest of that day.

The bitter cry of a red-shouldered hawk shrilled in the air. The black raven never stopped its gliding, back and forth, high over the canyon.

The squirrel huddled in her old nest in the den-tree.

The little fawn slept close to his mother, dry beneath an oak tree. The big buck had joined them that night and stayed until the sunlight made its way through the gnarled branches overhead.

Flying

Now there were only two young birds left in the nest of the big blue heron: only two beaks opening and snapping, two beaks clacking for food.

The birds grew with each day.

Soft gray feathers replaced the stiff pinfeathers, but the tousled cap of ruffled black on their heads did not change.

As they grew, the birds stretched their world beyond the safe circle of the platform. Each day they ventured farther and farther from the mass of woven sticks where they had been born: one step to the branch supporting the platform, one step into the swaying green boughs.

Day after day, the young birds worked their wings up and down, up and down, strengthening the muscles that must carry them.

At last, one morning the largest of the two birds, standing on the tip of a swaying bough, raised his wings. The soft wind moved under him. The world left his outstretched feet. His legs no longer held him.

Up, up, not too far from the safety of the branch, but enough.

The canyon shimmered with dark shadows below him. Blue sky stretched far overhead. A white cloud puffed in from the sea.

The young bird carried himself on his own slow-moving wings.

Then he glided, wings held wide, legs and feet searching. His black claws grasped, catching at a branch. He held tightly. The branch dipped and swayed for a moment, but the young heron balanced himself with half-open wings. Then he stood straight and still as he folded his wings to his side.

He had flown!

It took a long time to return. Standing on the end of the branch, the young bird stretched his neck forward, forward, out, out, until, like a thin bridge, it almost reached between the tree where he stood and the branch from which he had flown.

He pushed. His long legs raised him up.

He opened his wings and moved them very slowly, down, up, and then down again. Two easy, strong strokes. He was there. He had crossed the openness between the two trees.

Keeping his wings spread, he was able to move up the branch in short hops until he returned to the safety of his own platform.

Young herons and delicate white egrets were learning to fly in this way all over the rookery. The trees were filled with the blue and white half-walking, half-flying fledglings. They returned to their own nests only to rest and to eat the food which the older birds still brought from the lagoon.

The warmth of the summer days poured over the rookery. Shimmering heat waves rose from the deep floor of the canyon. The sweet smell of hot redwoods, bay trees, and sagebrush filled the air.

Wet fog crept down from the mountains at night, leaving the trees shining with its dampness in the morning.

The Last Days

One by one young herons and egrets spread their wings to leave their nests for the last time.

The older birds followed soon after.

The rookery grew quiet.

Only the young birds in the nest of the big blue heron, almost the last in the rookery to hatch, still waited: climbing, gliding, stepping from branch to branch as they moved up and down in the tall redwood tree.

Big Blue and the mother heron fished for many hours each day in order to feed the huge, hungry birds, who still could not fly to the water.

The quiet days passed. Then, one hot summer afternoon, when Big Blue returned to the nest, no young birds squawked as he landed, no bills opened to be fed. The platform was empty.

The mother heron, her work finished, did not return to the tall redwood tree after that.

Alone, at the top of the tree, Big Blue looked down on the empty nests where the herons had guarded their young and the beautiful egrets had preened their snowy-white feathers.

A full moon reached over the edge of the canyon, pouring gold through the black trees.

The little screech owl called. For the first time in many months the sound echoed through the stillness.

The gray squirrel leaped through the rookery inspecting the nests. There would be little excitement in the canyon for a long time to come.

The doe and the fawn grazed side by side in the shadows.

Big Blue sat hunched by the nest that he had successfully defended against the attacks of strong young birds.

He spread his great wings and rose, up, up, on the night

wind, a long black shadow stretched in the moonlight. Then, he too disappeared over the rim of the canyon.

In the morning the band-tailed pigeons returned to their places at the top of the tall redwood tree.

A WORD FROM THE AUTHOR

This account is the result of observations made over a three-year period at the Audubon Canyon Ranch on the Bolinas Lagoon, which lies some fifteen miles north of San Francisco, California.

When the ranch was threatened by the chain saw and bulldozer of a development builder, the Marin County and Golden Gate Audubon Societies joined forces to save the canyon, which contains the last major rookery for the great blue herons and American egrets in this area of California. Besides purchasing the 569 acres of the ranch, the Audubon Societies leased, from the Bolinas Harbor District, 369 acres of water and tidelands in Bolinas Lagoon. The lagoon not only provides a feeding ground for the nesting herons and egrets, but is, as well, an important link in the Pacific Flyway for wintering waterfowl and migrant shore birds.

The author wishes to thank all those who gave so generously of their help and advice in gathering information for this story.